THIS BOOK BELONGS TO:

_____

_____

Free Bonus Gift Giveaway!!

Sign up on explorearthursworld.com to receive your gif

10 WORLD WONDERS

A GUIDE FOR YOUNG EXPLORERS

GENE LIPEN

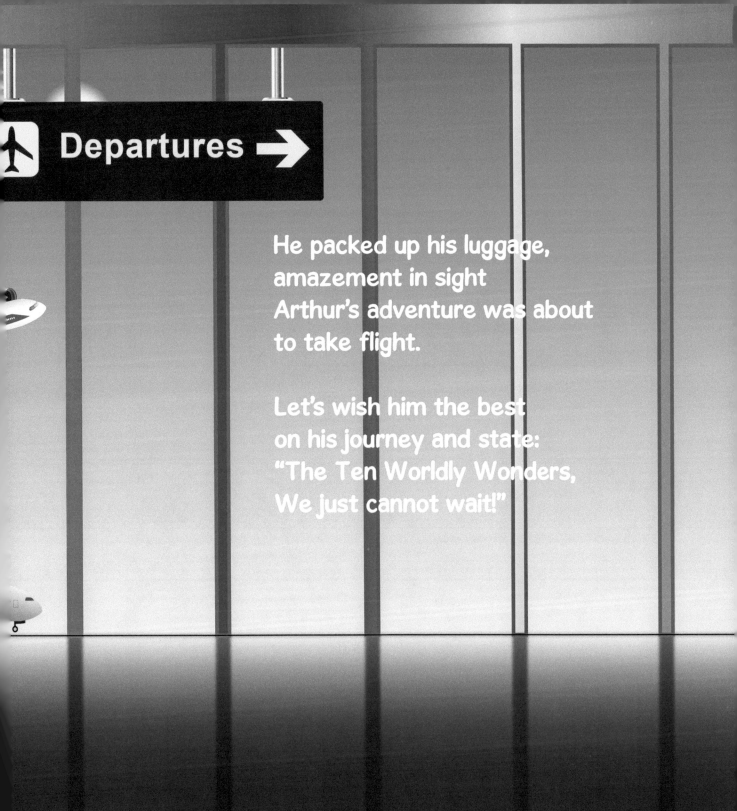

Departures →

He packed up his luggage,
amazement in sight
Arthur's adventure was about
to take flight.

Let's wish him the best
on his journey and state:
"The Ten Worldly Wonders,
We just cannot wait!"

What makes this a Wonder,
With views you can't beat.
The French Eiffel Tower stands 1000 feet
Four legs at the base and ten thousand to

Eiffel Tower

Do not try to climb it, it will trigger alarms!
It lights up the sky on a beautiful night
And has a view from above like no other in sight.
If visiting Paris is on top of your list,
The great Eiffel Tower is not to be missed.

In the city of Agra, this Wonder resides,
Made of white marble, with amazing designs.

taj mahal

A thousand elephants helped with construction,
It took twenty-two years to complete this production.
Protected by walls on three of its sides,
A beautiful garden will greet you inside.
Beloved and enjoyed by millions of people,
Stands Taj Mahal, famous Indian symbol.

If oceans have always been your fascination,
See the Great Barrier Reef of Australian nation.
Located in waters of the warm Coral Sea,
With breathtaking colors, I think you'll agree.
1400 miles is the stretch of this place,
This natural Wonder can be seen
from outer space.
With three thousand reefs
and 900 islands,
Let ocean's wildlife entertain you
in beautiful silence.

Like an Amazon River
   that flows through the wilds,
      The Great Wall of China stretches 1300 miles.
         Once used by its people as a form of protection,
         It is currently famous as a tourist attraction.
         Made of earth, stone, and brick,
         And at 30 feet wide,
            You can certainly walk on it—
               Dare to try?

Hidden in the deserts of magical Egypt,
Sits our next famous Wonder, which hides a huge secret.
Nobody knows in the world to this day,
How people constructed
this amazing display.

Pyramid of Giza

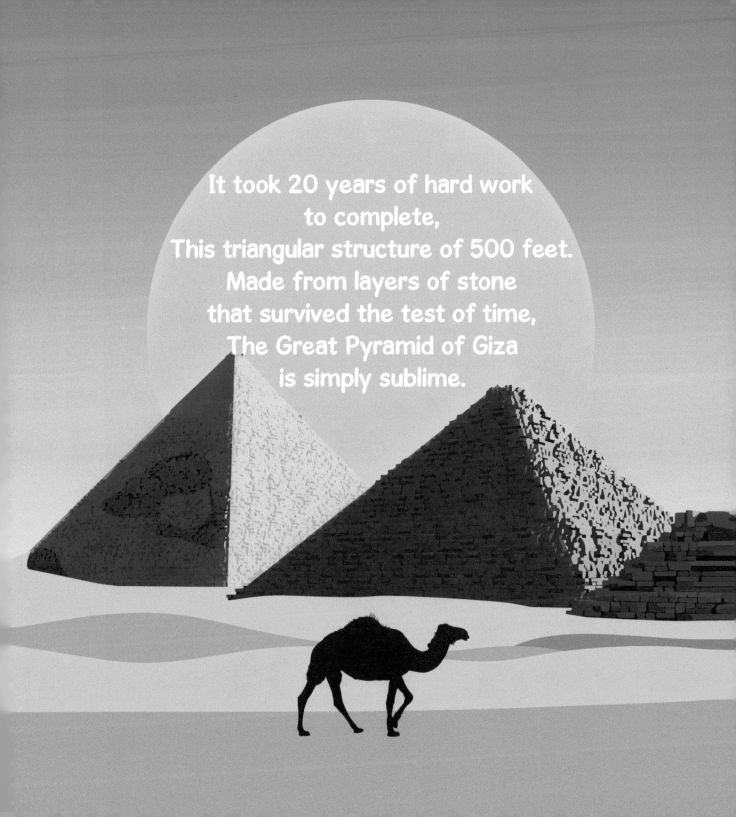

It took 20 years of hard work
to complete,
This triangular structure of 500 feet.
Made from layers of stone
that survived the test of time,
The Great Pyramid of Giza
is simply sublime.

On top of the world, in the greens of Peru,
Sits a magical site locals call Machu Picchu.
Amazing estate that it was in its day,
Its stories and legends
will blow you away.

Constructed by locals
in the year 1450,
People and animals
filled this royal city.
If you are in the mood
for exciting adventure,
Pay this place a visit
and reflect on its nature.

If blustery, Arctic cold wind is your calling,
You will find yourself mesmerized and falling
For the beauty and grace of the great Northern Lights
That cover the sky throughout the dark nights.

aurora

For centuries, people were shocked and amazed
By the crackling noises that Aurora makes.
Wherever you come from, near or far,
The magical colors will leave you in awe.

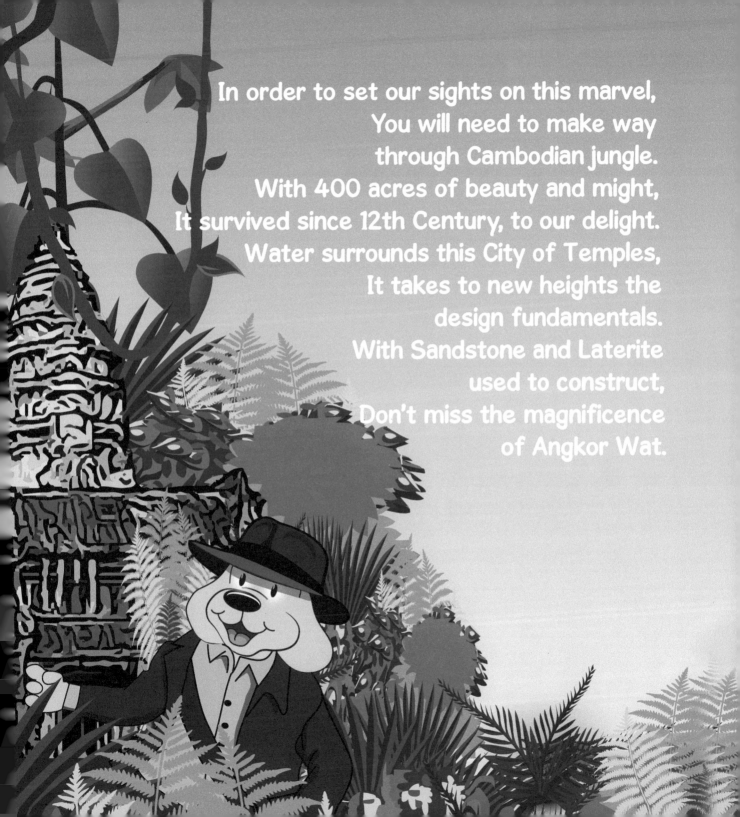

In order to set our sights on this marvel,
You will need to make way
through Cambodian jungle.
With 400 acres of beauty and might,
It survived since 12th Century, to our delight.
Water surrounds this City of Temples,
It takes to new heights the
design fundamentals.
With Sandstone and Laterite
used to construct,
Don't miss the magnificence
of Angkor Wat.

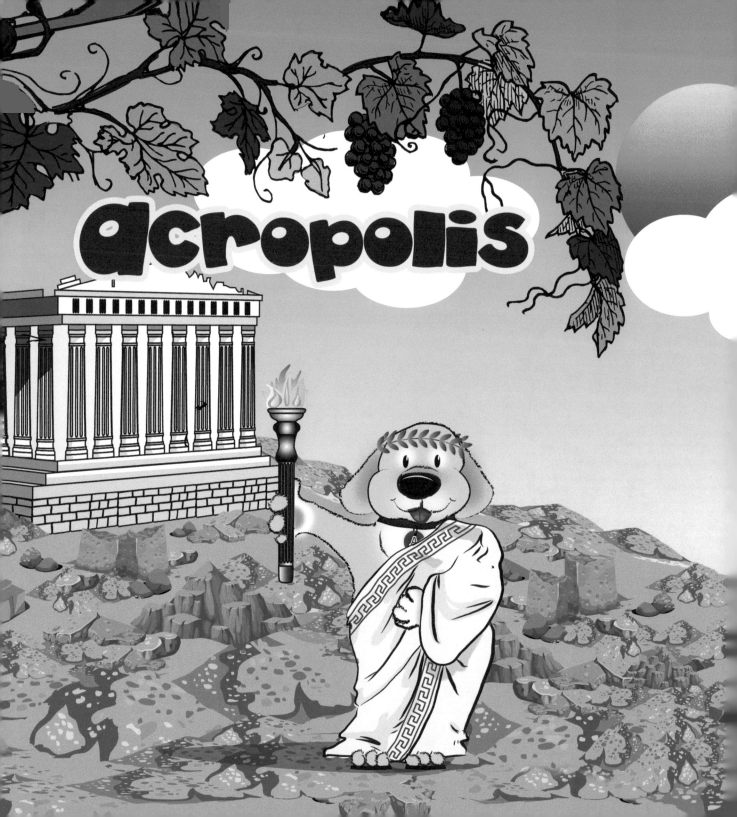

A site representing the glory of Greece,
Above the city of Athens, stands Acropolis.
This temple of Gods built atop a huge hill,
Its multiple structures will give you a thrill.
One of the buildings is famous and known,
Made of marble and limestone:
the grand Parthenon.
Feel on top of the world,
read the story and see
This astonishing symbol of Greek legacy.

Narrow passage through mountains gives us a clue:
In the deserts of Jordan and hidden from view,
Lives a Rose-colored city,
made of building-size stone.
In a magical place where great camels roam,
With nothing but sand and no water in sight,
This Wonder was born and became a bright light.
People would come for unique architecture,
But the city was used as a main trading center.
A great water system, the first of its kind,
Made this dry location distinctly designed.
Take a big breath and reflect for a moment,
And you'll also become a Petra proponent.

Our magical journey
has come to an end,
We've traveled all over
this fabulous world.
This story is ending,
but we all can assume,
Another Arthur adventure
will be coming soon!

Thank you for reading. If you enjoyed this book, pleas
consider leaving an honest review at your favorite stor

Check out more books about Arthur in
the Kids Books For Young Explorers series

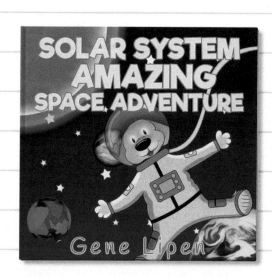

FUN COLORING PAGES

enjoy

I LIKE THIS BOOK, BECAUSE:

_____

_____

CPSIA information can be obtained
at www.ICGtesting.com
Printed in the USA
BVHW020009120122
625989BV00008B/450